SPECTRUM 2

30 miniatures
for solo piano

Compiled by Thalia Myers

SPECTRUM 2 was commissioned by Thalia Myers
with financial support from The Britten-Pears Foundation.

Winner of the Music Industries Association's
Music Publisher's Best New Product Award for 2000.

The Associated Board of
the Royal Schools of Music

CONTENTS

First published in 1999
Reprinted in 2000
The Associated Board of the Royal Schools of Music (Publishing) Limited
24 Portland Place, London W1B 1LU, United Kingdom. www.abrsmpublishing.co.uk

This collection © 1999 by The Associated Board of the Royal Schools of Music. The cover reproduction
of the manuscript of *Haiku* by Jonathan Harvey, Copyright © 1998 by Faber Music Limited,
is reproduced by kind permission of Faber Music Limited and Jonathan Harvey.

ISBN 1 86096 084 7

Cover design by Økvik Design. Music origination by Andrew Jones.
Printed in England by Caligraving Ltd, Thetford, Norfolk.

INTRODUCTION

Welcome to *Spectrum 2*: easier to play than the first collection and every bit as musically abundant.

The continuing purpose of the *Spectrum* series is to expand the contemporary repertoire of short, musically serious but unvirtuosic pieces for students, amateurs and professionals. An important part of this purpose is to encourage the emerging generation of players to explore new music as fearlessly as young people would have done 200 years ago. But these collections are aimed equally at musically inquiring amateurs and at professional players who enjoy playing fine music, regardless of whether or not it shows off a virtuoso technique.

I am delighted that all twenty of the original *Spectrum* composers, together with a distinguished further ten, agreed to contribute to this outstanding new anthology. As before, the works in this volume make no musical compromises and the stylistic range is enormous. All the contributing composers agreed to write pieces that would reflect their concert-music style, whilst remaining accessible to pianists of modest technical command.

Easy to play, but hard to write. Retaining, or distilling, a musical style in a piece no longer than ninety seconds, with severe limitations on texture, poses a very considerable compositional challenge. See for yourselves how this challenge has been met. Physically undemanding the thirty miniatures may be, but they are real music, as suitable for the concert hall as for the front room.

As with the first volume, bringing the idea of *Spectrum 2* to fruition has been a fascinating experience. My thanks to Matthew Greenall, Director of the British Music Information Centre, for a great deal of excellent advice. Much gratitude, too, to my students at the Royal College of Music Junior Department and at Royal Holloway, University of London, for being highly articulate guinea-pigs and for offering some inspired suggestions. I am grateful to The Britten-Pears Foundation for making, once more, a generous contribution to the commission fees. As before, working with ABRSM (Publishing) Limited has been enormously enjoyable. And to the thirty composers of *Spectrum 2*, my whole-hearted gratitude and admiration. I am confident that they will be richly thanked in the way that will please them best: performances, lots of them.

THALIA MYERS
September 1998

COMPOSER BIOGRAPHIES

ELEANOR ALBERGA

b. 1949 Jamaica. Trained as pianist and singer at the Royal Academy of Music. Spent three years performing with authentic African dance company and has sung with internationally celebrated Jamaican Folk Singers. Is also professional pianist. Compositional activity began with writing for London Contemporary Dance Theatre. This led to a wide range of concert music encompassing, besides electronic scores, works for orchestra, choral and chamber ensembles, and pieces for solo instruments.

AVRIL ANDERSON

b. 1953 Hampshire. Studied with Humphrey Searle and John Lambert at the Royal College of Music, at the New England Conservatory, Boston, and with David del Tredici in New York. Co-Artistic Director, with David Sutton-Anderson, of Sounds Positive ensemble. Has written works for orchestra, chorus, instrumental ensembles, solo instruments and voice. Composer-in-Residence, Young Place (London Contemporary Dance School). PRS Composer-in-Education 1997.

JULIAN ANDERSON

b. 1967 London. Began composing at age of eleven. Studied composition with John Lambert privately, then at the Royal College of Music; subsequently with Tristan Murail in Paris and Alexander Goehr in Cambridge. Has written orchestral music and works for chamber, vocal and instrumental ensembles as well as solo piano. Won 1992 Royal Philharmonic Society's Prize for Young Composers. Teaches composition at the Royal College of Music and is active as broadcaster and writer on music. His orchestral work 'The Stations of the Sun' was commissioned for and received its world première at the 1998 BBC Proms.

DAVID BEDFORD

b. 1937 London. Began composing when he was seven years old. Studied at the Royal Academy of Music with Lennox Berkeley and, in Venice, with Luigi Nono. In late 1960s played keyboards in Kevin Ayer's band The Whole World and collaborated with numerous rock musicians, including Mike Oldfield and Elvis Costello. Catalogue includes works for orchestra, chorus, instrumental ensembles, solo instruments and voice. Greatly involved in educational projects and creative workshops in UK and overseas.

RICHARD RODNEY BENNETT

b. 1936 Broadstairs, Kent. Began writing in early childhood and composed three string quartets by age of eighteen. Studied composition at the Royal Academy of Music with Howard Ferguson and Lennox Berkeley; later with Pierre Boulez in France. Now lives in New York City. Has performed and toured extensively as jazz pianist. Compositions include works for large variety of forces, orchestral, instrumental, choral and vocal, in addition to educational music, and film and television scores. Holds International Chair of Composition at the Royal Academy of Music.

DIANA BURRELL

b. 1948 Norwich. Read music at Cambridge. Spent several years as freelance viola player, as well as teaching, until a growing number of commissions in the 1980s led her to concentrate on composition. Educational activity has included working with and writing for COMA (Contemporary Music-Making for Amateurs). Has composed opera and works for a broad variety of orchestral, choral and instrumental ensembles; also solo instruments and voice.

PHILIP CASHIAN

b. 1963 Manchester. Studied at Cardiff University and at the Guildhall School of Music & Drama with Oliver Knussen and Simon Bainbridge. Director of Oxford Festival of Contemporary Music since 1993. Educational activity has included working with the London Symphony Orchestra, Britten Sinfonia and the Composers Ensemble. Teaches composition at Goldsmith's College, University of London, and Bath Spa University College. Has written for orchestra, chorus, instrumental ensembles, solo instruments and voice.

LAURENCE CRANE

b. 1961 Oxford. Studied at Nottingham University with Peter Nelson and Nigel Osborne. Lives in London and works as freelance editor and composer. Central to his output are three sets of songs to his own texts, which deal with people, places and incidents in an anecdotal style. Has written for a variety of chamber ensembles, as well as instrumental duos and solos.

JEREMY DALE ROBERTS

b. 1934 Minchinhampton, Gloucestershire. Studied composition at the Royal Academy of Music with William Alwyn and Priaulx Rainier. Has been active as a professional pianist, performing in chamber music and with singers. Teaches composition at the Royal College of Music, where he began deputising for Herbert Howells in the 1970s and was Head of Composition from 1992 to 1997. Output includes orchestral, choral and chamber music, as well as works for solo instruments and voice.

BRIAN ELIAS

b. 1948 Bombay, where he started piano lessons and began composing at an early age. Came to England in 1961. Studied composition at the Royal College of Music with Humphrey Searle and Bernard Stevens; also, privately, with Elisabeth Lutyens. Professional activity has included major commissions from the BBC and the Royal Ballet, and tutorship to post-graduate composition students at Goldsmith's College, University of London. Output includes orchestral and choral music as well as works for solo instruments, ensembles and voice.

MICHAEL FINNISSY

b. 1946 London. Started composing when he was four. Studied composition at the Royal College of Music with Bernard Stevens and Humphrey Searle and piano with Edwin Benbow and Ian Lake; later studied composition in Italy with Roman Vlad. As pianist, has commissioned and performed many new works by British composers. Has written prolifically for wide variety of forces: orchestral, choral, chamber, solo instrumental and vocal, as well as opera and dance music. Teaches composition at University of Sussex and at the Royal Academy of Music.

GRAHAM FITKIN

b. 1963 West Cornwall. Studied with Peter Nelson and Nigel Osborne at Nottingham University; later with Louis Andriessen in Holland. In 1985 co-founded The Nanquidno Group, four pianists at two keyboards, since when music for solo and multiple pianos has formed the central core of his work. Founded Graham Fitkin Group, sextet of strings, saxes and percussion, in 1996. Has written opera, music for dance and works for orchestra, instrumental ensembles, solo instruments and voice. Greatly involved in educational projects in UK and overseas.

MICHAEL ZEV GORDON

b. 1963 London. Studied composition at Cambridge with Robin Holloway and at the Guildhall School of Music & Drama with Oliver Knussen; further studies in Italy with Franco Donatoni and in Holland with Louis Andriessen. Plays the oboe. Professional activity has included teaching composition at the Royal Northern College of Music and at Durham University. Presently Fellow in Composition at the University of Birmingham. Output includes works for chorus, chamber ensembles and solo instruments.

JONATHAN HARVEY

b. 1939 Sutton Coldfield, Warwickshire. Studied at Cambridge and Glasgow Universities; privately with Erwin Stein and Hans Keller; later, briefly, with Milton Babbit. Plays cello. At the invitation of Pierre Boulez, worked and produced electroacoustic compositions at IRCAM, Paris. Catalogue includes music for wide variety of forces: operatic, orchestral, choral, chamber, instrumental and vocal, with and without electronics and tape. Honorary Professor of Music at University of Sussex and Professor of Music at University of Stanford, USA, for part of each year.

ALUN HODDINOTT

b. 1929 Bargoed, Glamorganshire. Composed and played violin from an early age. Studied at University College, Cardiff, and later in London with Arthur Benjamin. Founded the Cardiff Festival of 20th Century Music with John Ogdon in 1967, remaining its artistic director for over twenty years, during which time he was also Professor of Music at Cardiff University. Prolific output for many forms: operatic, orchestral, chamber, choral, solo instrumental and vocal.

GABRIEL JACKSON

b. 1962 Bermuda. Studied composition at the Royal College of Music, first in the Junior Department with Richard Blackford, later with John Lambert. Has written for orchestra and a wide variety of chamber, choral and instrumental ensembles, solo instruments and voice. Strong involvement with the visual arts has led him to work with film, and pieces based on works by artists Richard Long and Ian Hamilton Finlay. With writer Richard George Elliott, has produced a number of vocal and choral works.

NEIL KACZOR

b. 1967 Kidderminster, Worcestershire, and began composing at the age of ten. Studied composition at the Royal College of Music with Timothy Salter and electroacoustic composition at City University, London, with Simon Emmerson. In addition to fulfilling commissions for concert music, has worked with choreographers Darshan Singh Bhuller and Michele Durtnall; also with animator Riccardo Iacono. Output includes compositions for orchestra, chamber ensembles and solo instruments, as well as electro-acoustic music and soundtracks for film.

EDWARD McGUIRE

b. 1948 Glasgow. As junior student at the Royal Scottish Academy of Music received flute lessons from David Nicholson. Studied composition at the Royal Academy of Music, London, with James Iliff; later with Ingvar Lidholm in Stockholm. Plays flute with Scottish traditional folk-group, The Whistlebinkies, with whom he regularly records and tours internationally. Has composed for a wide variety of forces, including orchestra, chamber ensembles and solo instruments, as well as opera and ballet.

COLIN MATTHEWS

b. 1946 London. Read Classics at University of Nottingham, then studied composition there with Arnold Whittall; also with Nicholas Maw. In 1970s taught at University of Sussex and obtained Doctorate for his work on Mahler. During this time, also worked with Benjamin Britten and Imogen Holst at Aldeburgh. The core of his output is orchestral and he has been Associate Composer of the London Symphony Orchestra since 1992; has also written large body of chamber and ensemble music. Also active as record producer and is founder of NMC Recordings.

BARRY MILLS

b. 1949 Plymouth. Is mostly self-taught. Obtained degree in Biochemistry from Sussex University; later (also from Sussex) MA in Music, studying analysis with David Osmond-Smith and David Roberts and composition with Colin Matthews and Anne Boyd. Works as delivery postman in the morning and composes in the afternoon. Three CDs of his music exist on the Claudio Contemporary label. Has written orchestral and choral music and works for chamber ensembles and solo instruments.

STEPHEN MONTAGUE

b. 1943 Syracuse, New York. Educated in USA, at Florida State and Ohio State Universities. Has lived, as freelance composer, in London since 1974, and travels worldwide. As pianist, has performed and broadcast internationally. Has collaborated with sculptor Maurice Agis, composing multi-channel sound environments for Agis's giant inflatable sculptures. Output includes orchestral, choral, chamber, vocal and solo instrumental works (some with tape and electronics) as well as electroacoustic music. Has been Guest Professor at Universities in USA and New Zealand.

ANTHONY PAYNE

b. 1936 London. Before studying music at Durham University composed a number of works, then abandoned composition for some years. Became active as music journalist, continuing to work in this field after returning to composition in mid-1960s. Has published books on Schoenberg (1968), Frank Bridge (1984) and on his completion of Elgar's Third Symphony (1998). Output includes orchestral, choral and chamber works, solo instrumental and vocal music.

ROGER REDGATE

b. 1958 Bolton. Studied violin, piano, composition and electronic music at the Royal College of Music; also conducting with Edwin Roxburgh. Continued studies with Brian Ferneyhough in Freiburg, Germany, where he was also active as violinist and conductor. Has worked in the areas of jazz, film/TV music and performance art and is conductor and director of Ensemble Exposé. Has written for a variety of chamber ensembles and choruses as well as instrumental duos and solos. Currently Lecturer in composition at Goldsmith's College, University of London.

EDWIN ROXBURGH

b. 1937 Liverpool. Studied composition at the Royal College of Music with Herbert Howells, in France with Nadia Boulanger and in Italy with Luigi Dallapiccola. Later studied at St John's College, Cambridge. Is also professional oboist and conductor. Director of RCM 20th Century Ensemble at the Royal College of Music, where he teaches composition and conducting and holds the RVW Fellowship in Composition. Has written opera and orchestral, choral and chamber music as well as works (some with electronics) for solo instruments.

TIMOTHY SALTER

b. 1942 Mexborough, Yorkshire. Read music at St John's College, Cambridge. Studied piano with Lamar Crowson. As pianist has performed internationally with singers and instrumentalists. Also active as a conductor and is musical director of The Ionian Singers. Founder and director of Usk Recordings. Output includes music for orchestra and a wide variety of chamber ensembles; works for solo instruments, voice, and a large body of choral music. Teaches composition and performance studies at the Royal College of Music.

DAVID SAWER

b. 1961 Stockport. Brought up in Suffolk, where he was leader of Suffolk Youth Orchestra. Studied composition, singing and violin at University of York; later studied in Cologne with Mauricio Kagel, whose works he has both directed and performed. Much involved in theatre and visual arts, as performer and composer. Has been recipient of Fulbright Fellowship in Composition, Paul Hamlyn Foundation Award and Arts Foundation Composer Fellowship. Has written for orchestra, chamber ensembles and solo instruments; also music-theatre, dance, film and radio.

HOWARD SKEMPTON

b. 1947 Chester. Studied privately with Cornelius Cardew, a significant influence, both as a leading experimentalist and as a fine pianist. Has written over three hundred works, many of them short 'lyric poems' for piano or accordion; also music for ballet and orchestral, choral, vocal and chamber ensembles. Professional activity has included working in music publishing and playing the accordion.

DAVE SMITH

b. 1949 Salisbury. Read music at Cambridge University. In 1970s was member of the Scratch Orchestra and several composer/performer groups; later of ensembles specializing in Javanese classical and Albanian folk musics. Educational activity has included teaching at De Montfort University and working with COMA (Contemporary Music-Making for Amateurs). Plays with Gavin Bryars Ensemble. Output since 1983 has included much solo piano music organized into recital-length 'piano concerts', six of which have been completed.

JOHN TAVENER

b. 1944 London. As a child, composed and improvised at the piano. Entered the Royal Academy of Music as an aspiring concert pianist but decided to become a composer whilst still a student. Studied composition with Lennox Berkeley and, later, David Lumsdaine. Entered the Orthodox Church in 1977, since when he has absorbed the ethos of Orthodox liturgical music. Output largely vocal and choral music, but also instrumental and orchestral works. His music was performed at the funeral of Diana, Princess of Wales.

ANDREW TOOVEY

b. 1962 London. Studied composition with Jonathan Harvey, Morton Feldman and Michael Finnissy. Artistic Director of new music ensemble IXION. Diverse influences embrace poetry (Artaud, cummings, Rilke) and visual art (Bacon, Beuys, Miro, Riley, Rothko inter alia). Educational activity includes working with, and writing for, COMA (Contemporary Music-Making for Amateurs). Two CDs of his music have been issued on the Largo label. Has written operas and orchestral music; also works for chamber ensembles and solo instruments.

THALIA MYERS

b. 1945 Bath. Studied piano at the Royal College of Music with Cyril Smith and later with Ilona Kabos and Peter Feuchtwanger. Now combines an active career as a pianist, giving numerous première performances and broadcasts of new British music in Great Britain and abroad, with teaching posts at both the Royal College of Music Junior Department and Royal Holloway, University of London.

Nyanyushka's Song

JEREMY DALE ROBERTS

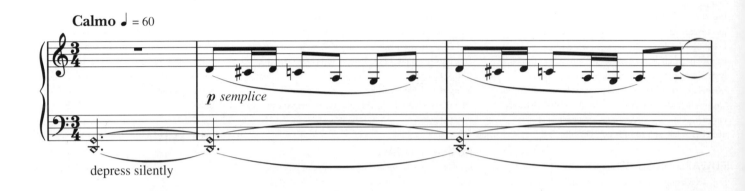

July 1997

The composer writes: 'This little piece should be played entirely without pedal; simply, but expressively. *Nyanyushka* is one of the many diminutives for the old Russian nanny.'

Any accidental affects the note it precedes for the entire bar.

for my mother

Slow Moon

PHILIP CASHIAN

7/8 Aug. 1997

Any accidental affects the note it precedes for the entire bar, but should only be applied to the stave in which it appears. Full pedalling directions have been given by the composer.

Only a wish away

ELEANOR ALBERGA

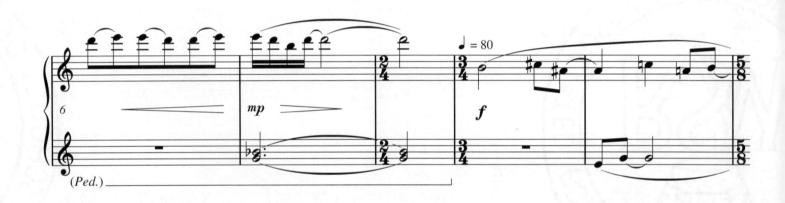

Any accidental affects the note it precedes for the entire bar, but should only be applied to the stave in which it appears. Full pedalling directions have been given by the composer.

AB 2713

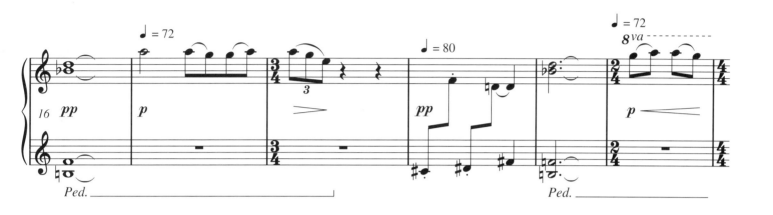

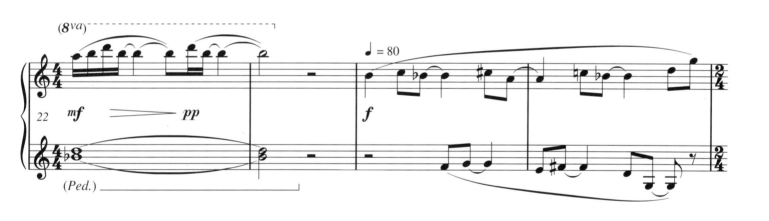

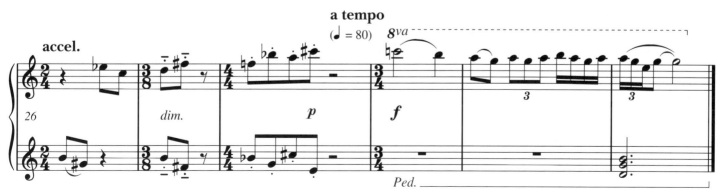

1997

Lizard

ALUN HODDINOTT

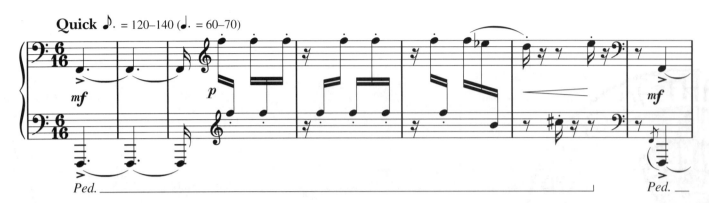

The composer writes: ' *Lizard* was suggested by a poem by the Welsh writer Gwyn Thomas:'
It's a Lizard/ Come out/ To warm its blood in the sun/ Small, mottled, stock still/ With skin like tissue paper/ Respirating energy.
Then a pizzicato/ Across the wall, across its sunlight:/ Another stop,/ Respires again.

Any accidental affects the note it precedes for the entire bar, but should only be applied to the stave in which it appears. Full pedalling directions have been given by the composer.

Aug. 1997

Happy Birthday

for Thalia Myers

High Ground

MICHAEL ZEV GORDON

Simple, flowing, flexible ♩ = *c.*112

sempre **p**, *cantabile, dolce e legato*

no pedal

The inverted mordents should be played on the beat, and on white notes only. The *8va* sign only refers to the notes in the right hand.
The pedalling directions have been given by the composer.

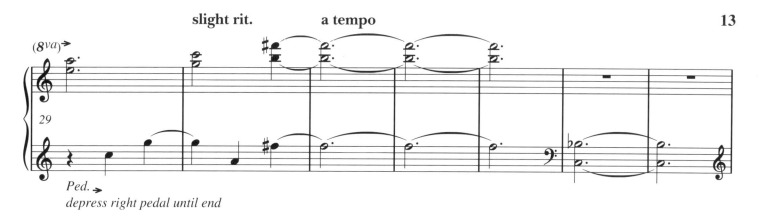

slight rit.   **a tempo**

Ped.
depress right pedal until end

sempre legato

(Ped.)

(Ped.)

(Ped.)

lunga

Crouch Hill, London, 30 Sept. 1997

arc

ROGER REDGATE

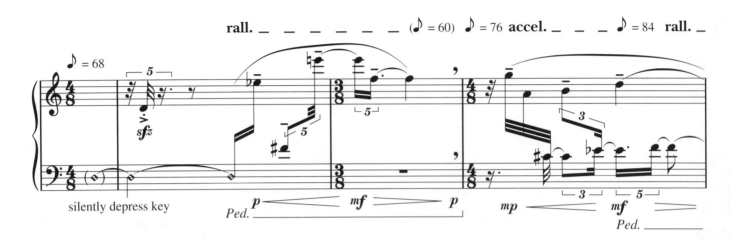

silently depress key

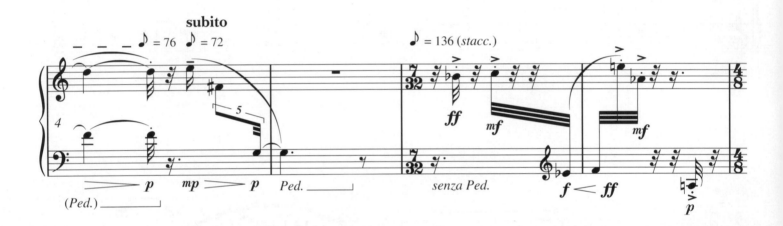

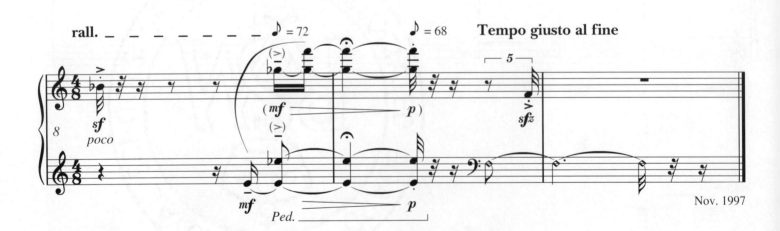

Nov. 1997

The composer writes: 'Any accidental refers only to the note it precedes. Full pedalling directions have been given.

Diamond-shaped note-heads (◊) in the first and last bars (L.H.) indicate that the key is to be depressed *silently* and held for the notated duration. The *sfz* attacks (one octave higher in the R.H.) will then activate the *silent* strings generating related harmonics.

Tempo markings are to be interpreted as an approximate guide only and can be treated with some degree of flexibility. After the initial tempo has been set, subsequent indications are seen as a means of articulating the expressive structure of the piece.

The comma (ꞌ) at the end of bar two is intended as a brief punctuation to end the first phrase and help place and emphasize the beginning of the second phrase.'

AB 2713

2/5/03

for Thalia

Tango

MICHAEL FINNISSY

With relentless elegance (♩ = 88)

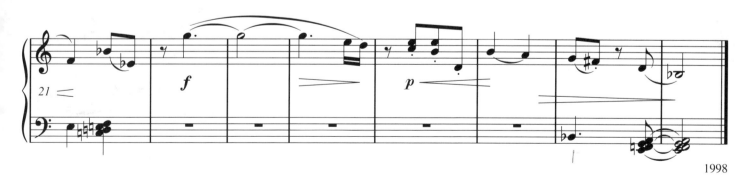

1998

Any accidental refers only to the note it directly precedes. Pedalling is at the performer's discretion.

AB 2713

Taking a line for a walk

RICHARD RODNEY BENNETT

Any accidental refers only to the note it directly precedes. The pedalling directions have been given by the composer.
The title is a quotation from the artist Paul Klee (1879–1940).

12 Jan. 1997

Cat being bold at first

TIMOTHY SALTER

Fearless; gradually becoming circumspect ♩ = c.112

London, 29 Sept. 1997

The composer writes: 'Cat being bold at first, thinking better of it, going for the prudent option.'

Any accidental refers only to the note it directly precedes. The pedalling directions have been given by the composer.

AB 2713

In Memoriam

NEIL KACZOR

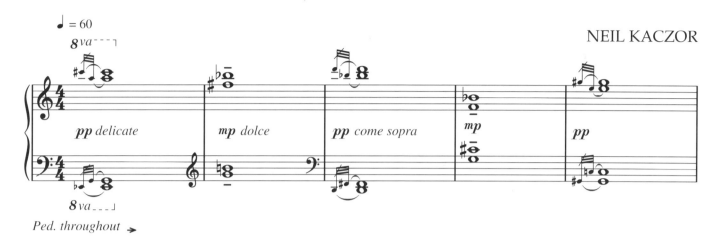

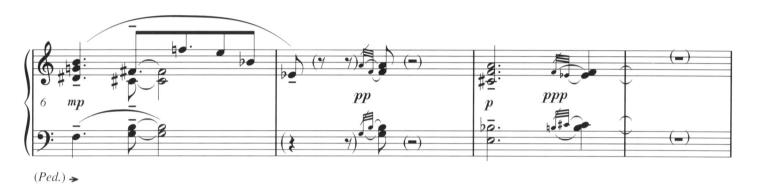

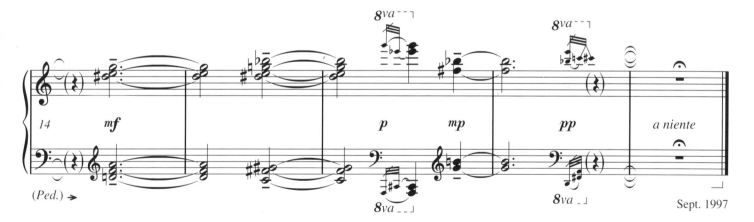

Sept. 1997

Any accidental refers only to the note it directly precedes. The pedalling direction has been given by the composer.

The grace-notes should be played on the beat. ♪♪♪♪ (bar 10) means accelerando within the beat.

Rosamund's March

COLIN MATTHEWS

Steady, not too fast ♩ = 63

+ = play with fist

May 1997

The composer writes: 'Pedalling (only in bars 13–22) is at the performer's discretion. The notation of 'clusters' is approximate – it doesn't matter too much if two or four notes are occasionally hit with the fist, as long as they are hit with some force! Note that for much of the piece the right and left hands have different dynamics.'

'Rosamund' is Colin Matthews' friend, Rosamund Strode, who was assistant to Benjamin Britten for many years.

Somewhere near Cluj

JULIAN ANDERSON

The composer writes: 'This piece uses a simple, folk-type melody, somewhat reminiscent of the traditional music found in the region of Cluj in Romania.'
Any accidental refers only to the note it directly precedes. Pedalling is at the performer's discretion.

7/6/02

for Toby

Tsunami

STEPHEN MONTAGUE

Pedal throughout

Ped. sempre (to bar 51)

* if top C unavailable, play top five white notes
** black note clusters – play with the side of a clenched fist

The composer writes: ' *Tsunami* is the name for a Pacific tidal wave caused by an underwater earthquake or volcanic eruption. Signs in most coastal buildings in New Zealand warn: *When you hear the alarm siren, do not go to the beach to watch! By the time you see it, it will already be too late to escape.* A *tsunami* can theoretically stack to a height of 66 meters (198 feet) tnd truvel the width of the Pacific rim at the speed of sound.'

The pedalling direction has been given by the composer.

AB 2713

(white note cluster)

(white note clusters)

(black note clusters)

R.H. gliss.

gliss.

*** play with palm of the hand

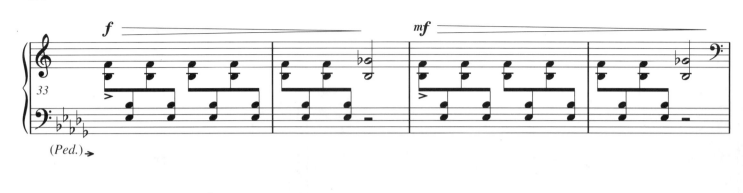

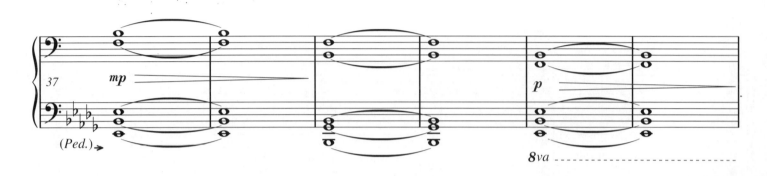

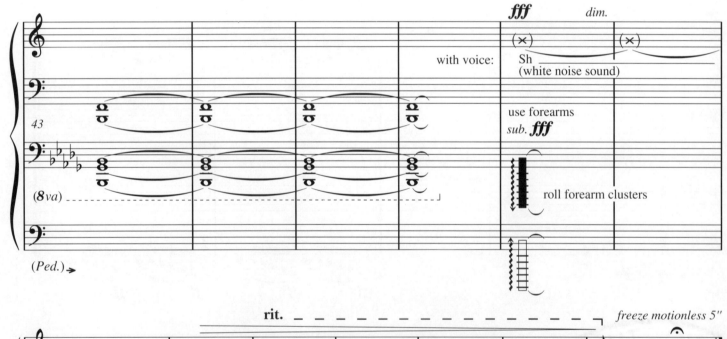

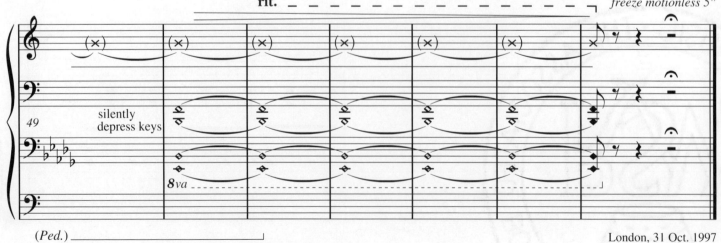

London, 31 Oct. 1997

Chorale for Howard Skempton

LAURENCE CRANE

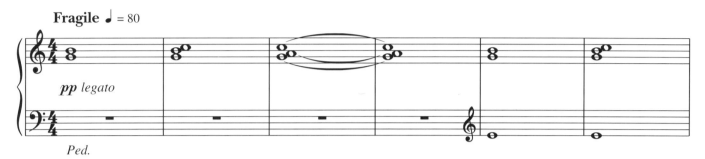

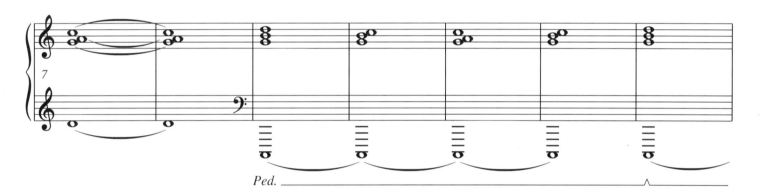

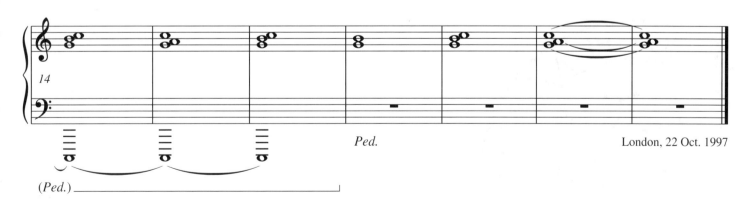

London, 22 Oct. 1997

The composer writes: 'This piece was composed to mark the 50th birthday of the composer Howard Skempton in October 1997. In bars 1–8 and 17–20 the pedal should be used discreetly to facilitate legato.'

Foglie d'Autunno
Autumn Leaves

EDWARD McGUIRE

The composer writes: 'A fast but sad and nostalgic piece in a new "romantic" vein, it gives much opportunity for expressive and delicate playing. There is an earthy rootedness in the deep sparse drones and passing exhilaration as the music moves into very different keys.'

Full pedalling directions have been given by the composer.

* tie last time only

Oct. 1997

Plaint

BRIAN ELIAS

Sept. 1997

The composer writes: 'The piece should be played quietly and atmospherically, maintaining the opening tempo throughout. The right pedal may be used lightly.'

AB 2713

Haiku

JONATHAN HARVEY

2/11

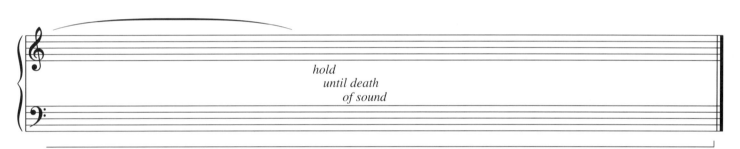

release pedal *visibly!*

12 Nov. 1997

The composer writes: 'I wrote more... and found myself in the unusual position of rejecting everything as superfluous, as diminishing the force of the idea. *Live* with the final E flat, it "contains" the other notes. And that there is *nothing* after it is perhaps shocking: the end defines the meaning.'

Full pedalling directions have been given by the composer.

for Howard Skempton

Tuesday

DAVE SMITH

The composer writes: ' *Tuesday* (and its companion piece *Bourke Street*) relate to an Australian expression – someone who 'doesn't know Tuesday from Bourke Street' is always confused. Both are from a set of short pieces dedicated to Howard Skempton (who is far from stupid). This set forms a part of the *6th Piano Concert.'*

Indicated articulation and dynamics are representative of the composer's performances. Other solutions are possible.

9 Nov. 1997

for Rebecca and Katherine Chandler

Little Dances

ANDREW TOOVEY

* mordents – on the beat – for more experienced players

The composer writes: '*Little Dances* was written while I was composer-in-residence at the Banff Centre, Canada, during the summer of 1997. It is dedicated to my young nieces Rebecca and Katherine Chandler who both love dancing and are training in ballet classes.
The piece contrasts different "dances", moods and textures.'

Any accidental affects the note it precedes for the entire bar, but should only be applied to the stave in which it appears. Full pedalling directions have been given by the composer.

AB 2713

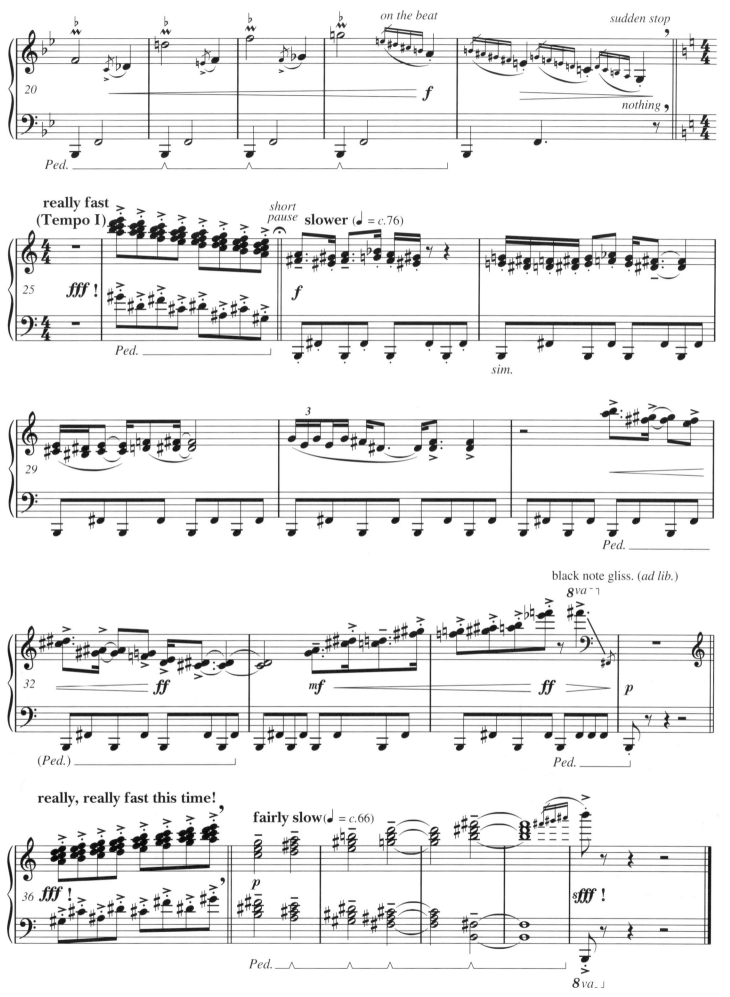

Banff, Canada, July 1997

2/11/0'

for Thomas

Sunset over Stac Pollaidh

DAVID BEDFORD

Nov. 1997

The composer writes: '*Stac Pollaidh* (pronounced Polly) is a mountain in the North-West Highlands of Scotland. The surrounding landscape is such that if you climb the mountain (it is a steep walk, fairly strenuous but very rewarding) the view from the top at sunset gives an atmosphere of peace and calm.

Try to play softly and calmly, and choose a comfortable speed. The left hand should be slightly less smooth than the right hand – almost like a soft drum. The grace-notes (known as "graces" in bagpipe music) should be played as quickly as possible before the beat.'

Pedalling is at the performer's discretion.

AB 2713

Clouds

BARRY MILLS

June 1998

The composer writes: 'In *Clouds* the right pedal is kept down over long spans of music, which allows one musical event to dissolve gradually into the next, so evoking slowly changing cloud patterns. Pauses, frequent changes of time signature and brief speeding up and slowing down in tempo add to the floating quality of the piece.'

Any accidental affects the note it precedes for the entire bar, but should only be applied to the stave in which it appears. Full pedalling directions have been given by the composer.

AB 2713

for Amber and Jonty

A Story Untold

AVRIL ANDERSON

The composer writes: 'Accidentals affect the pitches they precede for the entire bar but should only be applied to the stave in which they appear. The pedal should only be used where indicated and care should be taken to ensure evenness of touch between right and left hands.'

AB 2713

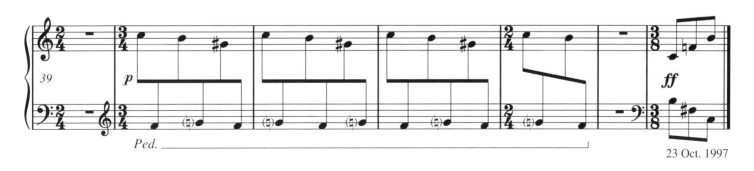

23 Oct. 1997

Hallowe'en

EDWIN ROXBURGH

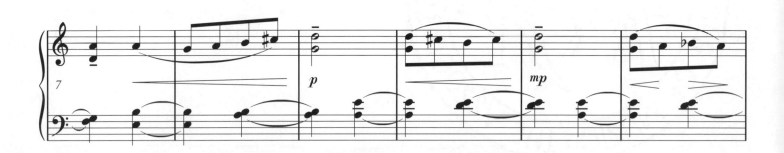

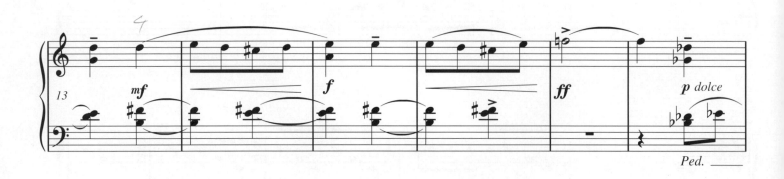

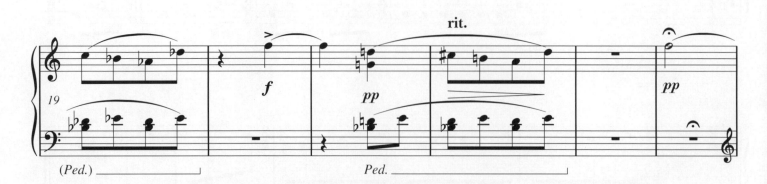

The composer writes: 'Technically, the piece uses varying figurations within the five-finger group, calling on independence of fingers as well as legato evenness. The mysterious nature of Hallowe'en comes through dynamics (including sudden surprises) and the winding and rather ghostly phrasing.'

Any accidental affects the note it precedes for the entire bar, but should only be applied to the stave in which it appears. Full pedalling directions have been given by the composer.

© 1999 by The Associated Board of the Royal Schools of Music

25 Oct. 1997

Micro-Sonata

ANTHONY PAYNE

The composer writes: 'Thalia Myers' request for even shorter pieces than had appeared in *Spectrum* made me think of writing a miniature sonata-form movement, with two little subjects, a tiny development and an infinitesimal coda. It should be played with rhythmic flexibility, so relax a little when you arrive at the second subject (bar 11), and the pedal should be used at the player's discretion to obtain a warm, clear sound.'

Accidentals affect the note they precede for the entire bar, but should only be applied to the octave in which they appear.

© 1999 by The Associated Board of the Royal Schools of Music

Oct. 1997

Tunch

GRAHAM FITKIN

use pedal discreetly throughout

The composer writes: '*Tunch* contains two contrasting strands of music. The first has a dark ostinato feel and is generally in the bass clef. The second is more plaintive, using simple melody and accompaniment. These two strands alternate throughout, with the ostinato figure rising up the piano at each reappearance to meet its counterpart. Tunch...a sort of Tea/Lunch meal.'

Any accidental affects the note it precedes for the entire bar, but should only be applied to the stave in which it appears. The pedalling directions at the beginning and at bars 31–34 have been given by the composer; elsewhere, pedalling is at the performer's discretion.

Jan. 1998

for Sofia

Zodiacs

JOHN TAVENER

The composer writes: 'Zodiacs is a simple and short piece for Piano Solo. The concept is far from simple, however. The combination of tones seems to be symbolized by the Tree of Life – for all the Zodiacs begin alike, and then branch out symmetrically from the centre; the marriage of Heaven and Earth takes place in the *mandorla* where the celestial and terrestrial Zodiacs intersect. *Zodiacs* is dedicated to my youngest daughter, Sofia.'

Any accidental refers only to the note it directly precedes. The pedalling directions have been given by the composer.

27 Feb. 1997

l'escalier

DAVID SAWER

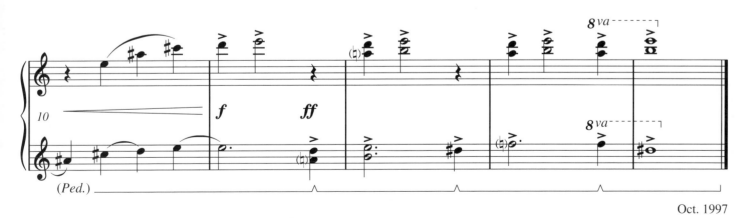

Oct. 1997

Any accidental refers only to the note it directly precedes. Full pedalling directions have been given by the composer.

to Liam

The Little Bear
No. 3 from 'Constellations'

DIANA BURRELL

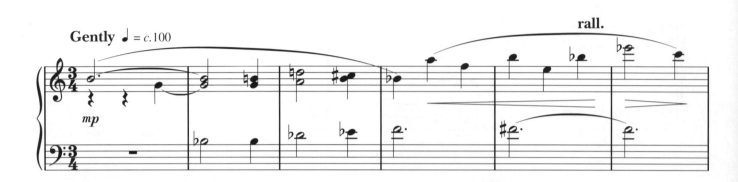

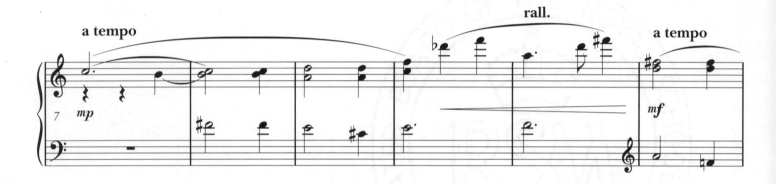

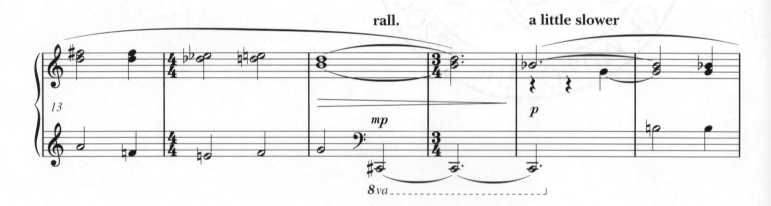

1997

Any accidental affects the note it precedes for the entire bar, but should only be applied to the stave in which it appears. Pedalling is at the performer's discretion.

AB 2713

October Monody

GABRIEL JACKSON

26–29 Oct. 1997

The composer writes: 'Pedalling is at the performer's discretion. Grace-notes should be played as short as possible and before the beat.'

for Thalia Myers

Arpeggio

HOWARD SKEMPTON

3 Oct. 1997

The composer writes: 'This piece requires a light touch. The sounds should "ring", as suggested by the open ties (*sim.* means 'and so on'). Use of the right pedal as indicated ensures the necessary fullness of harmony.'

AB 2713

10:00